SNOWDON SHEPHERD

SNOWDON SHEPHERD

FOUR SEASONS ON THE HILL FARMS OF NORTH WALES

KEITH BOWEN

Foreword by

JAN MORRIS

PAVILION

Acknowledgements

My thanks to all the shepherds and farmers who have
shown such patience and kindness towards me, giving so generously
of their time and sharing their knowledge and experience.
Without their invaluable help this book would never have
been completed.

First published in Great Britain in 1991 by
Pavilion Books Limited
196 Shaftesbury Avenue, London WC2H 8JL

Copyright © 1991 Keith Bowen

Designed by Lee Griffiths

ISBN 1 85793 0657

Printed and bound by Printer Portuguesa, Portugal

10 9 8 7 6 5 4 3 2 1

CONTENTS

FOREWORD

On the western fringe of Europe stands Wales, and in the north-west corner of Wales is the heartland of a most ancient people. There in medieval times the kingdom of Gwynedd was a last bastion of the Welsh against the conquering English; there Welsh champions from Llywelyn the Great to David Lloyd George have been nurtured; there the Welsh language thrives still, in everyday conversation as in traditional verse or rock lyric.

Indeed everything most truly Welsh fights on in what is now the county of Gwynedd, defying the worst that tourism and English settlement can do. By a happy irony Caernarfon the county town, site of the most terrible of all the castles that the English built to subdue the country, is now perhaps the most thoroughly Welsh of all Welsh towns. In the twentieth-century county, as in the twelfth-century kingdom, every development is sure to find an indigenously Welsh response or resistance – sometimes hidden beneath layers of Anglicization, but vigorous nevertheless, and expressing itself in means that vary from the burning of holiday cottages to the writing of poems for *eisteddfodau*. Choose the right Gwynedd pub on a Saturday night, and you will find it vivacious with the music, the laughter, the arguments and all too likely the inebriation of young Welsh people, speaking, singing and thinking Welsh.

The innermost fastness of Gwynedd is the mountain range called Eryri, and the symbolical centre-piece of all is Yr Wyddfa, the highest peak in Wales – Snowdon to the English. Not only legend, but history, custom and loyalty have always attended this famous summit, and in the foothills and valleys around a hardy race of hill-farmers has evolved, over the centuries, patterns of life that are all its own. It is to this grand place, among this tough and witty people, that Keith Bowen has gone to produce what is not only a work of art, but a celebration of Welshness itself.

For *Snowdon Shepherd* is a book of several kinds. On one

level, of course, it is a collection of exquisite pictures by one of the most distinguished of contemporary Welsh artists. On another it can be consulted almost as a primer of Welsh sheep-farming techniques, illustrating month by month how the flocks are bred, grazed, sheared and sold. But in a deeper sense it is also an allegory. The most widely-known word in the vocabulary of the Snowdon shepherd is *cynefin*, meaning as an adjective 'familiar', as a noun 'habitat'. It refers generally to the Welsh sheep's inherited knowledge of its own grazing boundaries, beyond which it will not stray, but it applies too to everything that this book represents between its lines and lovely colours: the steadfastness of a community, the un-changing strength of a countryside, the power of a tradition and the character of a people.

Jan Morris
Trefan Morys
Cymru

PREFACE

It's a hot, dusty day, and I'm sitting on top of the wall look-ing down at the shearing gang working their way steadily through the mass of sheep. Gradually, I begin to understand the sequence of positions that they adopt to shear each sheep. But as each position only lasts for about fifteen seconds, I work on three or four different sketches at once, adding to and building up each one as its position comes round.

The day wears on and gets hotter, but the pace doesn't ease off, neither does the number of sheep seem to get any smaller. The men shout up at me: 'Remember to paint in the sweat.' Jack Bach replies: 'That's not sweat, that's beer.'

By early evening the job is finally coming to an end, and one of the sheep is offered to me for shearing. Thinking of how Rembrandt's pupils would act out the pose that they were painting, so as to understand better the movement, I accept the offer in the hope of a good drawing. But all it does achieve is a good laugh. I'll stick to drawing.

To get back to the beginning. Why the fascination with this particular subject? Well, I've been kicking around the Welsh hills for over twenty-five years, and from early days in flappy, wet tents, the place for me has had a tremendous visual appeal. You don't have to choose the subject, for in a way it calls you; but you must have an affection for it, and feel a sensi-tivity towards it. Anyway, there's hardly much point in spending so much time on something that you don't like. As Constable wrote: '– old rotten Banks, slimy posts, and brick-work. I love such things,' and later: 'But I should paint my own places best – Painting is another word for feeling.'

And what does it feel like to be a sheep? The thought did occur to the young Thomas Hardy who went down on all fours amongst a flock of sheep to find out. My initiation came about less gracefully, when I was pushed off my sketching stool, paper and charcoal flying, and came face to face with a large, horned and woolly head. A variation on the now classic Parliamentary quip came to mind: "It was like being savaged by a wet sheep." I know the feeling.

Keith Bowen 12.7.90

OCTOBER

The farming cycle usually begins in October with the selection of the new flock. To restock the flock, the farmer carefully selects from his existing ewe lambs, and never buys on the open market. This selection is crucial as these sheep will be in the flock for the next four years, making up about a quarter of it.

A hill farm where the sheep run on the open mountain retains its own permanent flock, which is tied to one part of the mountain by heredity. By instinct a sheep knows its boundaries – in Welsh, *cynefin* – and will not stray. The ewe knows its part of the mountain and passes on this sense to her lambs. There are always four generations of sheep on the mountain.

October is also the month of the ram sales. It is not good for a farmer to keep too many of his own rams because of the problems that can be caused by inbreeding. *'You can't put a price on a ram. If you get two buyers who are interested in the same one, they're going to stick. If they both fancy it, then the price will just go up.'* And also: *'They say that if the ram is a bit redder, has more kemp, then it seems to have a bit more spirit, seems hardier, more fiery – just like red-headed people.'*

SNOWDON FROM LLYN YR ADAR

When buying a new ram a farmer will check the ram's teeth – in particular that his bottom teeth do not overlap the top palette – and his testicles, semen and feet. A white, masculine head, with the horns well out, some reddish kemp – a hairy white or red fibre – around the neck, good bones, strong shoulders, and close-knit wool to make the ram waterproof are features considered important. The ram's heredity and where he is from is critical.

Winter dipping takes place in October. The dip is to prevent scab, mites, and lice. Scab gets under the wool and debilitates the sheep, and their mites will hatch out in spring if dipping is not carried out. A ewe with lice will scratch her fleece, so that patches of bare skin show and wool hangs off. By shearing time, if she is left to scratch, a ewe will have pulled off all her fleece.

'The worst time for sheep is when the dip freezes on them; then sometimes you wonder if the weaker ones will stand it.'

'No, I've never seen scab, and I don't want to.'

'THE RAM IS HALF THE FLOCK.'

MOVING SHEEP

MOVING WATER

Scattered throughout the mountains are small, long-disused, sheep-pens. These are the remnants of an ancient style of shepherding in which small numbers of sheep, with no *cynefin*, were bought to stock the hills. Over the summer months the shepherd would closely keep watch over a dozen or so newly purchased sheep, having herded them within a particular area of the mountain, and return them to the pen at night, where he would sleep, with his dogs across the entrance. Through habit, the new sheep would eventually stay and graze within their new territory.

Since the nuclear accident at Chernobyl, all movement of sheep must be checked and cleared by the Ministry of Agriculture, Fisheries and Food. Every sheep is scanned for radioactivity by placing the probe on its rump. Three readings of ten seconds each are taken, and an average calculated.

The yearlings are now moved off the mountain to winter on more luscious and softer lowland pasture, so that they can have a good, strong start for the harsh winters they will face on the hills. But before they go to 'tack' – the winter pasture – they must all be dipped, dosed, drenched and vaccinated.

TRYFAN: AUTUMN SUNSHINE

NOVEMBER

The sheep are gathered from the mountain, and brought down to the lower pasture, so that the ram can be put to them. On Snowdon the gathering takes two days: on the first day the sheep on the lower slopes are gathered, then on the second day the top half of the mountain is cleared.

About half a dozen men and their dogs are needed to clear the mountain. One goes along the Bwlch Main ridge to the summit, a couple more work their way over from Y Lliwedd, and another takes the middle ground from the top of Bwlch y Saethau. When the weather is bad gathering can be difficult, as the sheep will be sheltering behind boulders or tucked up in hollows. But today it is still and warm on the tops, and the valley below is covered in thick cloud and mist. The steep buttresses of Clogwyn Du echo to the calling and whistling of the shepherds, the barking of the dogs and the bleating of the sheep as they are flushed off the high rock walls to join the ever-growing numbers that are being herded into Cwm Tregalan and then down into Cwm Llan.

WINTER DIPPING

EARLY MORNING LIGHT ON BWLCH Y SAETHAU: THE START OF GATHERING

The working dogs used on the mountain must have a good bark, and are entirely different from those seen at a sheepdog trial. It would be easy to lose sight of a dog as it drives the remaining sheep from among the rocks and boulders over half a mile away, but a bark lets you know where he is.

The sheep are now pushed gently along the top of Clogwyn Brith, and further over onto easier ground, where they can descend towards the mountain gate. Where the ground is steep the shepherds take care not to hurry the sheep, holding the dogs back, as the flock moves slowly down until over 1,500 ewes and lambs are on the lower pasture.

The wether (castrated) lambs are now sold for slaughter, while a small number of selected rams from the flock are kept for breeding, along with any rams bought at last month's sale.

The ram is now put to the ewes, so that the first lambs will arrive in early April. Gestation lasts 147 days, and the timing of the birth is traditionally calculated as five months forward and

From Bwlch y Saethau: Crib Goch, Moel Siabod, Y Lliwedd.

five days back. A mature ram of four or five years will serve between fifty and eighty ewes, a younger ram about thirty.

The rams follow the ewes around, putting their head in the air, and curling their top lip as they scent the odour from the ewes' rear ends. A ewe comes into season every seventeen days, and this odour signals that she is ready to mate.

The belly of the ram is painted with a red, oily raddle (red ochre) which marks the ewe's rump when she is served by the ram. Later the colour of the raddle will be changed, so that the ewes which are going to lamb later can be easily identified.

After a head count the sheep from the lower slopes of Snowdon are sent back up to their grazing ground with the rams. Both rams and ewes will spend the winter on the mountain. The sheep from the higher ground around the summit, are kept lower, otherwise the ram might not get to them all, scattered as they would be across the steep slopes of this storm-ravaged mountain, here at the very heart of Eryri – the place of the eagles.

MOEL HEBOG: FIRST SNOW

DECEMBER

With the onset of winter storms, any ewes that have been missed in the gathering will be forced down on their own by the bad weather. They will now need shearing, but as there are usually only one or two, it is not worth setting up the machine, and they are sheared by hand. As it is now becoming colder, it is important to leave more of the fleece on the ewes, and the hand shears are ideal for this job.

Until thirty or forty years ago, hand shearing was the normal practice, as machine shearing had not come into common use. Many men were needed, each sitting astride a bench, with the sheep placed on its back between their legs.

'As a boy, my job was to bind the legs, and place the sheep on the bench where the men sat down to shear. But then it was someone else's job to take it away, and take off the string.'

STONE WALL: DRWS-Y-COED

SHEARING BY HAND

TREFOR

AROUND THE HAYRACK

JANUARY

It takes three acres of mountain pasture to support one sheep, and so extra feed must be taken up to them when conditions are severe.

The Hardy Welsh Mountain breed has to be extremely tough to survive the winter conditions on the open mountain, and it must wander far in search of grazing.

The sheep will sense the approach of bad weather, and take shelter. The shepherd must move them out of sheltered hollows and onto more exposed land so that drifting snow does not bury them. Wet and freezing snow is heavy and could suffocate the sheep, although under light, powdery snow they can survive for three or four days by scratching into the ground and, if need be, eating their fleece. In such conditions dogs are used to locate sheep buried under snowdrifts.

'Hard frost and ice are worse than snow, because they can't scratch. I remember in '62 carrying and feeding ivy, and you had to break the ice every morning for them to have water. A lot died that year from lack of water.'

ERYRI: THE SNOWDON RANGE FROM THE SLOPES OF GLYDER FAWR

MOEL SIABOD FROM BWLCH RHIW'R YCHEN

(OVERLEAF) CLENNENAU: FROZEN FIELDS

WINTER FEEDING

FEBRUARY

Feeding is still the main job. If the weather becomes too severe the sheep are forced down off the mountain in search of food. Sometimes hunger will drive them to eat bracken and rhododendrons, which will kill them unless the shepherd gets to them quickly and administers salt and water to make them vomit.

The method of feeding is different on every farm. Some farmers prefer hay to silage, as a bale of hay is much easier to carry on the steep mountain slopes. Others take cereal blocks on three-wheeled bikes, for the ewes will now need more feed and nutrition to support the rapidly growing lambs that they are carrying. However, some farmers now use only the portable liquid feed: *'I haven't used hay for three years now. The trouble with hay is that they stand around the rack. Don't go off and roam like they should be doing. There's too much bulk in them, so they just sit there on the wet ground.'*

THE BROCKEN SPECTRE: SNOWDON FROM CRAIG CWM SILYN

RAM AT THE LICK

As winter continues and the ewes approach lambing time, the liquid feed is taken on to the hills two or three times a week. The sheep run towards the tractor as it makes its way uphill, then crowd around the shepherd as he refills the container. Liquid feed is high in sugars, proteins, vitamins and essential trace elements, and tastes a bit like a combination of treacle and cough mixture. However, the sheep show ingenuity when wanting to increase their intake, and flick the ball around with their front leg, in this way stimulating the flow of liquid across the surface of the ball. Some farms use blocks, a hardened form of the liquid, but others fear that young teeth could be loosened with the continual pressure on the block.

EVAN

DROVER BRIDGE: PONT RHYD Y PORTHMYN OVER AFON TAIHIRION

MARCH

The weather is still unpredictable: warm and quiet one day, snow and gales the next.

'Between back-end and the beginning of lambing it's a bit slack, and you have to look for things to do. I know there's plenty of things to be done.'

As well as feeding the shepherd will inject the ewes for diseases, and dose them for worms. Other jobs that need tackling include clearing and cutting drains, checking walls, and putting up new fences.

It is also time to catch up on paperwork: tax returns, VAT receipts, and grant applications. Next month, with the onset of lambing, there will be little time for such things.

Isolated and derelict cottages are to be found throughout the hills. Their stone walls and stark gable-ends are rapidy fading remnants of a way of shepherding that is now long gone: summer spent high in the hills at the *hafod*, and then back to the valley and the *hendref* for winter.

DERELICT FARM BELOW SNOWDON

APRIL

This is the busiest time of the year, when the shepherd goes short on sleep and long on walking. The yearlings are now back from 'tack' and are put on the hill.

A good shepherd makes sure he knows his sheep and understands their behaviour, as this can save lives. He will be constantly checking the ewes as they approach lambing, watching for complaints such as 'staggers', and, where the symptoms occur, injecting with calcium to get them on their feet again. Usually the younger and less experienced ewes are brought lower down the mountain, in case they need any assistance.

While constantly walking around the flock, the shepherd looks for signs of any ewe beginning to labour. She separates herself from the flock to be on her own, and starts to paw the ground restlessly with her front feet.

The normal position of the lamb in the womb is with its front legs and head ready to come out first. In this case the ewe will give birth without needing assistance. But the shepherd will know when things are not going smoothly and will make an internal examination to establish the position of the lamb. Posterior and breech presentations are when the lamb is facing the wrong way around with back legs out or tucked in respectively. These lambs are delivered backwards.

Sick lambs are brought inside to be bottle-fed, and are often kept in a cardboard box by the warmth of the kitchen stove until they are strong enough to rejoin the flock.

The lamb might need some help in getting on its feet. One way is for the shepherd to hold it by its back legs and gently swing it to and fro, then rub its back, or clear the mucus from the nostrils with a straw.

After an assisted birth the shepherd helps the exhausted ewe and lamb to form a bond by rubbing her nose into the lamb. The ewe now gets to her feet quickly to show that she has suffered no harm.

The ewe will eat her afterbirth, which has a very high nutritional value. Then she will start to lick her lamb clean and dry, so that it does not get cold: the biggest killer of lambs is hypothermia.

The lamb gets to its feet quickly, driven by instinct to look for milk. It must have milk within thirty minutes, and would die within twelve hours if deprived of it.

Having found the milk, the lamb will now take in the colostrum, which contains all the essential nutrients and antibodies specific to the diseases in its flock. The ewe recognizes her lamb by its smell and the lamb recognizes its mother by her call. They must now return to the flock, where there is safety in numbers.

When a ewe loses a lamb she naturally becomes a potential adoptive mother, and another lamb is quickly sought

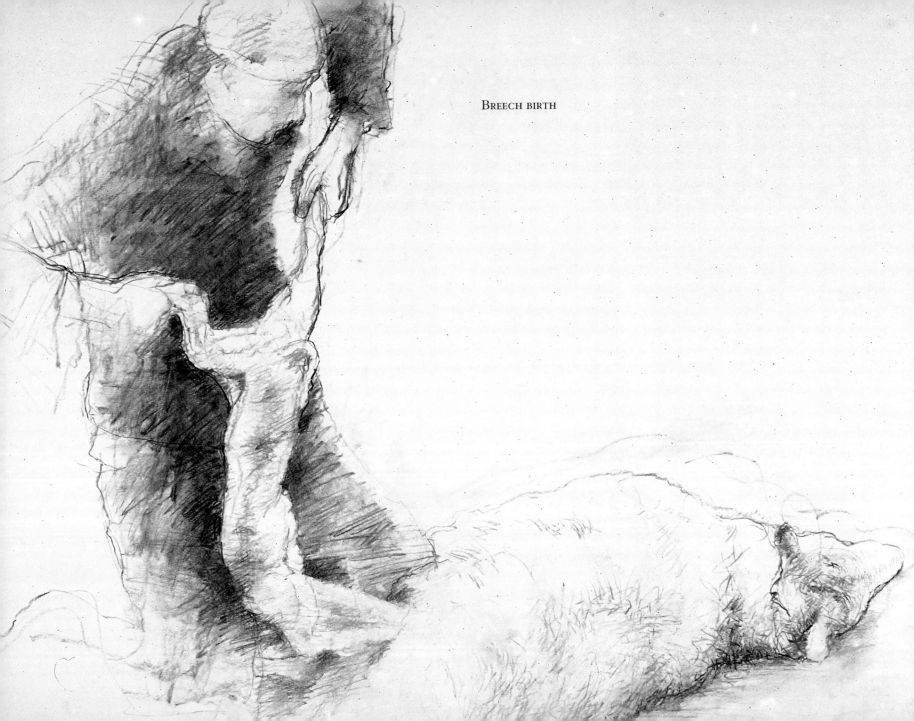

BREECH BIRTH

as a replacement. When an orphan is not available, twin lambs are sometimes separated, the stronger lamb being taken as it is better equipped to withstand the temporary upheaval. The shepherd works quickly to skin the dead lamb, and puts its coat on the foster lamb so that to the mother it smells like her own. They are kept close together for a day or two, until the mother smells her own milk on the new lamb. The dead lamb's coat can now be removed, and the mother will accept the lamb as her own.

Orphan lambs must quickly be found mothers, or they will tend to form a bond with any parent-figure, however improbable.

A large part of lambing is continually walking around to check the flock. The shepherd must move quickly over steep and difficult country, walking miles and ascending and descending thousands of feet in one day, if he is to watch the flock properly. *'See them rushes? There could be something the other side, laying down. So you have to go there.'*

'I have to come right up to the wall, to satisfy my own conscience. Anything could be tucked away here.'

THE FIRST SUCKLE

SKINNED LAMB

THE NEW COAT

THE WRONG MOTHER: SHEEPDOG AND ORPHAN LAMB

ROBIN

A RARE SIGHT: A BLACK EWE WITH HER TWINS: ONE WHITE AND ONE BLACK.

PEDIGREE BLACK WELSH MOUNTAIN EWE AND HER FOUR-WEEK OLD TWINS

Black sheep occur naturally in mountain flocks, but they bear little relationship to the pedigree strain, which has had most of the hardiness bred out.

Black wool is soft but hard-wearing, requiring no dyeing, and when mixed with white wool forms a grey yarn.

CLOSE GRAZING

Cattle and sheep graze happily together on the mountain. The cattle improve the ground with the manure, and graze on the long, rough hill grass, which the sheep will not eat, preferring the shorter grass. In turn the sheep-droppings fertilize the ground, as it is very high in potash.

(OVERLEAF) THE LAST OF WINTER: SNOW ON SNOWDON AND TRUM Y DDYSGL

'ALL IN THE APRIL EVENING.'

MAY

Lambing continues, but at a less frantic pace. In fact, one or two lambs will not arrive until the summer months, and May is the time when losses can occur unless a constant watch is kept.

After six weeks the lambs must be dosed to prevent worms and intestinal parasites. The ewes' tails must be docked to prevent maggots and blow-fly.

The ewes and lambs that have been kept lower are now taken up on to the mountain. They are transported separately, but must be brought together again quickly once on the mountain. At this time the lambs which have been on the mountain are gathered for counting and marking.

Today many farms do not castrate their ram lambs, but some still do, in the belief that this improves the flesh for slaughter next winter. Modern castration does not cut the lamb – it simply severs the internal cord to the testicles: the most hygienic and least painful method available.

As the wether lambs grow bigger, some of the ram lambs are selected for their potential breeding qualities and will be put to the flock when they have matured.

Sheep from upland farms are now ready to go on to the mountain for summer grazing. Before they go the boundary walls must be checked and repaired after the winter storms. The rain and the frost will bring the stone down if there is a hole within the inside of the wall that has not been filled. Also, when one sheep jumps the wall it will pull down a stone, then other sheep follow and the rest of the wall collapses, creating a gap. One way to prevent this is to place stones crossways on the top, so that the stone's edge will catch the sheep's brisket bone and prevent it going over.

'It's not so much to keep your sheep in, as to keep others out.'

To repair a collapsed wall you pull all the standing stones away, down to the very large ones at the foundation. They are then replaced from the side, the gaps filled in with smaller stones which are also placed under larger stones as stabilizers.

Some of the walls are five and a half feet high. Pressure is built up from a foundation width of about three feet to a foot in width across the top.

Standing among a mass of fallen stones, the shepherd can select the exact one he needs as he rebuilds the wall.

'It's an art. Either you can build walls or you can't.'

PUSHING PAST THE BIG ROCK, AND UP ONTO THE MOUNTAIN.

The first batch of ewes to be put on the mountain for summer are the barren and those that have aborted their lambs. They will have been sheared and marked beforehand. Barren ewes are identified by their frisky habit of jumping around and head-butting each other: *'You see, there's nothing in 'em.'*

The sheep are pushed up to the mountain wall, where a halt is called while the shepherds unplug the gap. Small stones are taken away until the gap is cleared, and the sheep are pushed through. The gap in the wall is then refilled.

THROUGH THE WALL AND OUT ONTO THE MOUNTAIN

Before the lambs are put on the mountain they must be ear-marked. This is essential if the shepherd is to identify his particular flock, and every farm has a different combination of marks. The shepherd will always know his sheep by their ear-mark, not just the paint mark on the fleece.

The traditional way to earmark is to use a razor-sharp knife. *'But unless you know what you're doing, you'll end up cutting your thumb.'*

The first recorded use of these pens dates from 1779. They were built using the local stone found scattered around, and today seem to be an integral part of the landscape. They are yet another reminder of the shepherding ways of yesteryear. One wonders how long the modern concrete and breezeblock constructions will last, and whether they will ever grow to be as sympathetic to their natural surroundings as stone pens.

CUT TIP	A POLL	A THREE CUT NOTCH
A NIP	A CHIMNEY POINT	A HOOK
A ONE CUT LACE	A FORK	A SLIT
A TWO CUT LACE	SPLIT	A KNIFE NICK
A SKEW	SPLIT INTO THREE	A LATCH NOTCH
A STUMP	A FOLD NOTCH	A HOLE

SHEEP-PENS: DRWS-Y-COED

RAIN STORM: MYNYDD DRWS-Y-COED

'RUB PIG FAT ON THE WELTS OF YOUR BOOTS. THAT'LL STOP THE WET GETTING IN.'

JUNE

The average mortality on a hill farm is around 10 percent, but it would be higher without regular walking around and checking on the flock. A ewe could be on her back and need help, or a bleating ewe could signal that her lamb is stuck in a wall or burrow. The saying goes: 'The dog that walks, gets.'

On the mountain, twins are not regarded as a good thing, since the ewe cannot always be guarding both lambs, to which foxes and crows present a particular threat. *'With some of these ewes, the fox couldn't get near them; they're so protective. But with twins, they can't do the job so good. They've got to be here, there and everywhere.'*

A fox will go for a weak lamb and will even drag it out of its mother's womb as it is being born. *'In five years I've only seen about five foxes on the top, but you can smell where he's been. It's like a sticky smell. Once you've had a whiff of it, it's always there.'*

'Now there's an instance for you. I don't know every ewe or else I'd be a bloody magician, but you know most. And there was one the other day, by the top of the incline there. I knew she had twins. Well anyway, the following day I remembered about her; I had a look and she only had one lamb – the other had gone. So, you see, Mr Foxy had been.'

Crows too will spot any weak lambs in the flock and attack. *'It's the weak ones that always go. And the bloody crows, it's easy pickings for them.'*

RESTING AGAINST THE SHADE OF A WALL

THE ONE-EYED EWE

'This ewe fell on her back in a ditch, and couldn't get up. I'd seen her two hours before and she was fine; but by the time I came around again she was down, and the crows had already taken one of her eyes out. I carried her back to the barn, and put her on some straw. I filled the old saucepan full of water, and she drank it dry. I did it three times before she'd had enough. That's fifteen pints. I gave her some penicillin and left her on her own, without her lamb to bother her. And now she's fine; back in the field grazing. They must be tough.'

'The gap at the top of the crook should be no bigger than the width of three fingers.'

Occasionally a sheep will graze by jumping from ledge to ledge, ending up in the middle of a crag, and not able to move. It will stay there until it becomes too weak and dies, or simply jumps off. If he decides to attempt a rescue, the shepherd usually waits until the ewe has grown weaker, when there is less chance of him being pushed off the crag.

'This is the only way to bring one off the mountain. It's your shoulders or a wheelbarrow.'

DIPPING LAMBS

Dipping is carried out two, sometimes three, times a year. Many years ago, a policeman would always be in attendance to see that things were carried out correctly. Prevention is better than cure, and this summer dip is to prevent blow-fly, which can attack the rear end of the sheep. A fine day is needed, so that the dip has a couple of hours to dry on the fleece. It is important that each lamb and sheep is totally submerged in the dip, including its head.

THE OLD SHEEP WASH, CARNEDDAU

Until about forty years ago, it was general practice to wash sheep about three days before shearing. This took out the dirt and oil from the fleece, which made it easier to shear by hand. Also, a better price was paid for the washed than the unwashed fleece. If, because of wet weather, the sheep could not be shorn, within a week to ten days after the first wash, the procedure would have to be repeated.

This practice has now died out with the advent of machine shearing, and because of the negligible difference between the price of washed and unwashed fleeces.

HAY BARN

When it is a good summer, hay is still made in abundance, but many hill farms must buy it in, keeping their land for grazing. 'Big Bag' silage is more popular than ever, as it can be cut and made when wet. Some call it 'the biggest revolution in farming in recent times', but others still prefer hay, as it has less bulk and moisture and is more portable for feeding on the hill.

JULY

Shearing is still the biggest communal working and social event in the hill-farming year. Neighbours join together to shear up to seven or eight hundred head of sheep in a day.

This practice is not as widespread as it used to be, as gangs of contractors, often New Zealanders, now work their way from farm to farm during the summer with the local men helping with the catching and handling.

What has not changed is the weather needed: it must be dry. *'If the wind is from Moel Hebog, and you can hear the waterfall, it's guaranteed to be a good day.'* Or: *'If The Wyddfa looks too near, then you can be sure the weather will change later in the day.'*

Since first light, men and dogs have been on the tops rounding up the sheep and gradually pushing them down the mountain. Nearly five hundred head of sheep are now in a field alongside the farm, and as it is still early morning the sheep are continually moved around to dry the dew off them, then herded together into the pens for sorting.

The mass of sheep is gradually sorted, to select the ones that are to be sheared. Some stray sheep from neighbouring farms will have been gathered and are now penned separately. Later in the day their owners will arrive to take them away.

The Hardy Welsh Mountain breed is numerically and economically the most important breed of sheep in the country. Welsh sheep represent seventeen percent of the total of all EEC sheep, and outnumber people in Wales by about three to one. On occasions such as this the figure seems a little higher.

THE GATHERING

INTO THE PENS

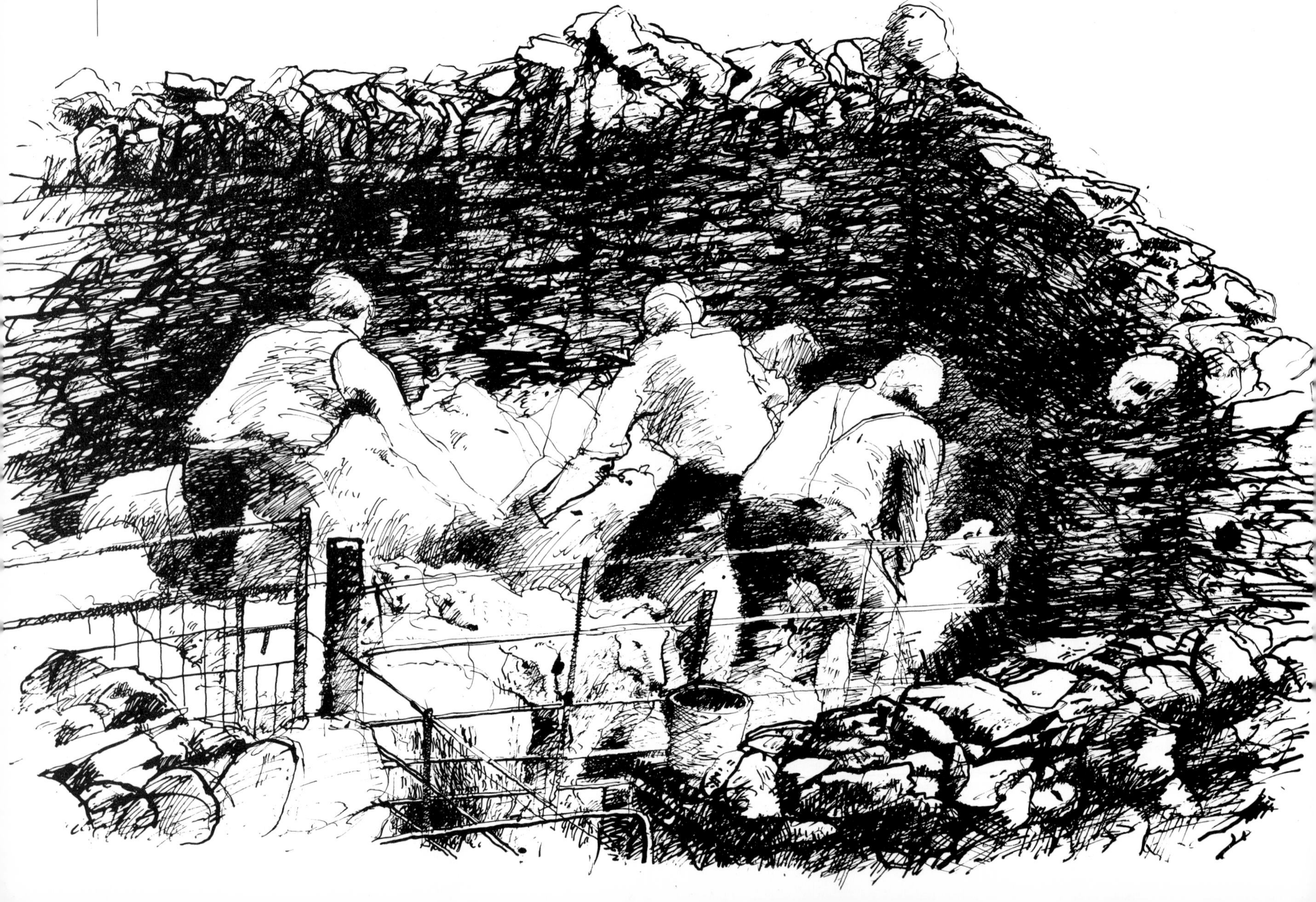

SORTED AND READY FOR SHEARING

The day is hot. Flies and dust are coming off the sheep. The shearer wipes his arms and face with a towel, then catches the next one, holding it by its neck and front legs. He pushes it through onto the shearing stage. The pen door bangs shut. The sheep is facing out, leaning against the man's legs. She is relaxed, sensing his confidence and experience. He presses his counter again, and grabs the pull-cord to the engine. The motor starts, and he's off again, the first 'blow' (combful) going down the belly from the front leg.

It takes forty-six blows to take the fleece off a Hardy Welsh Mountain sheep. The method is called the Bowen Style, and was introduced in 1957 by the guru of modern shearing, the New Zealander Godfrey Bowen.

The shaft from the engine to the handpiece can be either of rubber, which makes it flexible, or solid, which makes it lighter to use. The solid shaft has a spring at the top to bring it back. The sheep has to be moved around on the board, to get the cut exactly right. On a new board you can see a round mark where the sheep has been turned. If you are off this mark, then you will not be able to shear.

The ram will be pleased to be rid of his fleece, and will not be bothered by the cold at night. Within twenty-four hours his skin will have doubled in thickness, the oil and lanolin in it protecting him from the cold. During one day's shearing about four combs will be used. These are detachable from the handpiece. The combs come in different shapes, known as Hustler, Top Flight, Fine Wool, and Heiniger.

The Hustler comb is light and preferred for use earlier in the season. But as the season develops and the wool rises off the skin a Top Flight comb is more suitable.

SHEARING STUDIES

SHORN RAM

Shearing is definitely a young man's game. With the back down straight and flat, all the strain should be on the top of the legs. It is important to keep your back warm and protected from any cool breezes by wearing a woollen vest or a wide elastic belt.

The men change out of their working boots into soft trainers, slippers, or work in their bare feet on the shearing stage. The feet slide under the sheep to get a purchase, and boots would be too heavy.

All their clothes are covered in a brown-black greasy stain, and their usually hard hands have now gone smooth and soft with the lanolin from the wool.

'Another three blows and she'll be done. As it's curved, this blow's called the "boomerang"; it's on the last side: the "money side".'

'WE SHEEP COME WOOLLY, AND GO SHORN.'

LUNCHTIME

Throughout the day the women have been working hard preparing food and supplying drinks. They have been up since before six, and breakfast is ready by eight, after the gathering. Then comes the eleven o'clock break, followed by a large three-course lunch at one. Throughout the hot afternoon, orange squash and water are in continuous supply, and as another tray of drinks is brought out from the kitchen, the men shout: *'It's hot out here.'* The immediate response is: *'It's hot in there too.'* A halt is called for a short break of tea and Welsh cakes at about four o'clock. Finally, at eight o'clock in the evening, the men can sit down to a supper of cold ham and salad, knowing that the job is at last complete.

MARKING

Marking is carried out with an initialled iron stamp, handed down and particular to each farm. Years ago warmed, black pitch was used. *'In the old days, a bit of wool was left on, so it was better for the mark to hold to.'* Today shearing is done closer to the skin, the marking fluid is washable, but not from the rain, and comes in all colours.

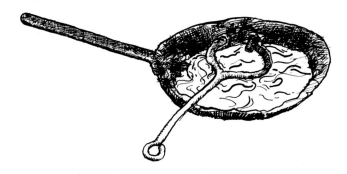

WRAPPING THE FLEECE

Each sheep produces an average of about three pounds of wool which is used in the making of blankets and carpets. As each fleece is worth just over a pound, the wool is now of secondary importance, but is still a good source of extra income to the farm.

The hairy white or red fibre known as kemp is present in the wool. It will not absorb dyes and is not regarded as an asset; but kemp, and an attendant coarser fleece, are seen as an advantage where hardiness in the sheep is needed on the mountain.

Wool has a natural springiness and resilience, always returning to its original shape – the only natural fibre with this quality. It is also flame-resistant, so that if you were to put a match to a fleece it would smoulder rather than burn.

FULL SHEETS

The wrapped fleeces are put into the wool sheet, which can contain up to two hundredweight of wool. About six wooden skewers are pushed through the top of the sheet, the centre skewer going in first, to tie up the top. The wool sheet is then dragged into the barn to await collection and at last a long, hard day is at an end.

AUGUST

The lambs must now be weaned off the ewes, so that they have time to come into season by next year. The ewes are sent up to the poorer pasture higher up the mountain, while the lambs are kept down to fatten on the better, lower pasture before they are sent to market. The ewes' milk will now dry off, but if it continues there is a danger of mastitis.

Routine dosing is carried out every six weeks, and the ewe lambs are given three separate vaccinations to protect them against a variety of diseases including pasteurellosis, lamb dysentery, braxy, tetanus, black disease, pulpy kidney and struck. But after they have had two teeth, they will need only one annual booster injection.

WORKING THE DOGS

The mothering ability of the Hardy Welsh Mountain ewe is renowned. Her natural thrift and milkiness make her give all she has to her lamb. By the end of the summer many ewes come off the mountain lighter in weight than their lambs.

The draft ewes (four-year-olds) are now selected for the September sale. They are now too old to survive the hard mountain conditions and so are bought by lowland farms, where they will thrive on the low-lying pasture and give lambs for at least another four years.

Before the sale, the teeth, feet and udders are checked. If any teeth are missing, the ewe is termed 'broken-mouthed' and rejected. Sheep have teeth only on their lower gums. They have lambs' teeth up to eighteen months, which are replaced by two permanent teeth. At two and a half years these teeth are flanked by two more, and then two more again every year, until there is a maximum of eight teeth: 'full mouth.'

THE ANNUAL SHOW: PRIZEWINNERS AND OLD FRIENDS

Mot

The dogs have a good natural working and herding instinct. Their characteristics are different from those of trial dogs: they show more spirit and have a good bark, revelling in the hard work demanded of them throughout the year.

SEPTEMBER

Work continues with dipping against scab, dosing ewes against fluke and checking for footrot. But the draft ewe sale has come around: the biggest and most important sale event of the year. Presentation is important, and much pre-sale grooming is carried out up to the last minute.

The auctioneer is keen to start as the first lot are herded into the ring:

'Somebody to get me started quickly. Thirty? Thirty pounds to get me away. Thirty-one. Everyone is guaranteed correct. Thirty-two.

Thirty-three. Big strong ewes aren't they? Built like lions. Thirty-three. And a half. Four, and a half. Five. Thirty-five. Is there any advance on thirty-five? Sold.'

The first lot has gone, and the second lot is already in the ring. The pace of bidding is brisk, with no lull in the proceedings, as today there are eighty-two lots to get through, amounting to over two thousand head of sheep.

As well as being a commercial event the sale has its social side as a meeting-place for old friends.

THE PRE-SALE INSPECTION

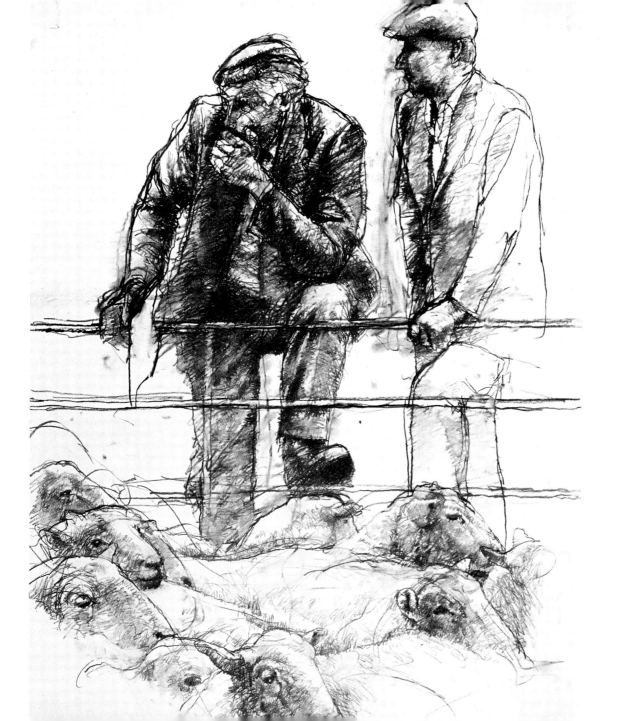

Some 450,000 Welsh Mountain draft ewes are sold annually. The minimum of shepherding needed, together with a low purchase price, makes them good breeding stock for lowland farmers.

'Stand on to get me away. Lot 29. Four-year-olds. Eight teeth. Eight more than I've got. They're out of the clouds, over two thousand feet above sea level, gentlemen. Big sheep for the money. Fill the ring, don't they? You can take one lot or two.' The bidding is brisk, and soon mounts up. The auctioneer turns to the farmer, and back to the microphone again: 'Do your best slowly, he says'. So the bid continues until the lot is sold.

The auctioneer pushes on through the lots, his voice never tiring, as his assistants on either side keep watch for fresh bidders and the farmer stands by expectantly.

CWM NANTCOL: STONE SHED

CWMYSTRADLLYN: TIN BARN

THE SHEEP HAS GIVEN MAN WORK, FED HIM, AND CLOTHED HIM.

SNOWDON FROM THE WEST: EVENING SUNLIGHT

'Live life as if you would die tomorrow,
Farm as if you will live forever.'